BOEING 727

Paul R Smith

Copyright © Jane's Publishing Company Limited 1987
First published in the United Kingdom in 1987 by
Jane's Publishing Company Limited
in conjunction with DPR Marketing and Sales
37 Heath Road, Twickenham, Middlesex TW1 4AW, England

ISBN 0 7106 0474 2

Printed in the United Kingdom by Netherwood Dalton & Co Ltd

JANE'S TRANSPORT PRESS

Cover illustrations

Front: **Air Atlanta** (CC)
Air Atlanta was a privately-owned carrier established in May 1981.
On 1 February 1984, the airline began scheduled services on Atlanta-
Memphis and Atlanta-New York routes, later adding services to
Philadelphia, Tampa, Miami and Orlando. On 3 April 1987, Air
Atlanta suspended services and filed for Chapter 11 bankruptcy
protection. The company had been operating as part of the "Pan Am
Express". *(P Hornfeck)*

Rear: **Northwest Airlines** (NW)
Northwest Airlines was established in August 1926, when it was
awarded a mail contract covering the Chicago-St Paul route. The
airline currently provides services to Hong Kong, Japan, South
Korea, the Philippines and Europe, as well as providing an extensive
US network of services. In 1986 the latter was greatly expanded
when Northwest purchased Republic Airlines. A fleet of Boeing 727,
747, 757, DC-9 and DC-10 aircraft is maintained, as well as various
other turboprops that make up the "Northwest Airlink", a group of
third-level airlines that feed passengers to regional destinations. The
company also has an order for up to 100 units of the Airbus Industrie
A320, as well as over 30 A330 and A340 types. *(P Hornfeck)*

Below: **Air Guinee** (GI)
Air Guinee, the state-owned flag carrier, was formed in 1960, with
Czechoslovak and Soviet assistance. The company operates a
network of scheduled passenger and cargo services from Conakry to
various domestic points, as well as to Sierra Leone, Liberia, Mali and
Senegal. Its fleet consists of IL-18, An-12, An-24, Yak-40 and
Boeing 737 aircraft. Although no longer operated, 3A-GCA, a 727-
100, is seen here at Conakry Airport. Rather forlorn it sits, in its
colourful livery, minus all three engines. *(P Bish)*

Introduction

The Boeing 727, first trijet introduced into commercial service, became in its time the best-selling civil airliner in history. Officially announced on 5 December 1960, following discussions with many US airlines, the first orders came from Eastern Air Lines and United Air Lines. They each ordered 40 aircraft of the 727-100 variant. Boeing estimated that it would sell a maximum of 250 units; amazing really, since the final figure stood at 1832. The production line ceased in August 1984. Of the total number sold, 548 were for overseas orders, whilst the rest went to US customers. Its peak sales year was 1965, when 193 were ordered. That dropped to 38 in 1981, and to just one in 1983. Production of the 727 has finished because airlines need a more economical aircraft for medium-range routes than the trijet, with its three-member flight deck. Its successor is the twin-engined Boeing 757. By mid-1983 this fleet of versatile trijets was carrying 43 million passengers per month. The first 727-100, a production model, made its inaugural flight from Renton Field on 9 February 1963, the second followed on 12 March 1963, and four aircraft were used for an intensive 1100-hour test flying programme that led to FAA certification on Christmas Eve of that year. Deliveries for airline crew training had begun two months earlier, and scheduled services with the type were started by Eastern Air Lines on 1 February 1964, followed five days later by United Air Lines. There were seven variants of the 727 built. The -100 was the standard passenger transport for up to 131 passengers, while -100C was a convertible cargo passenger version, announced in July 1964. The 727-100QC was the same as the latter, except that by using palletised passenger seats, galleys, and advanced cargo loading techniques, complete conversion from all-passenger to all-cargo configuration could be made in less than half an hour. A 727M version was made available for military use, in roles such as carrier on-board delivery, flight refuelling tanker, assault transport, staff command and aero-medical transport. A "stretched" version was announced in 1965, with basic accommodation for 178 passengers. The 727-200 had a fuselage extension of 3.05 m (10 ft), as well as more powerful engines. First flight of this type was in May 1967, followed by its certification in September 1967. Delivery to Northeast Airlines began in June 1972, and by September of that year total orders for the aircraft had reached 1000. The 1800th example was delivered to Pan Am on 26 May 1982, with the final passenger 727 going to USAir. The second "life" for the 727 began in 1970, when the Advanced 727-200 was announced. This version had a new "wide-body" interior, extended range and increased gross weight. The final variant, the -200F, is an all-freight aircraft, ordered mainly by Federal Express.

I would like to thank everyone who has assisted in the preparation of this book, and my sincere gratitude must go to the various photographers who have contributed material.

TABLE OF COMPARISONS		
	BOEING 727-100	**BOEING 727-200**
Max accommodation	131	178
Wing span	32.92 m (108 ft 0 in)	32.92 m (108 ft 0 in)
Length	35.41 m (135 ft 2 in)	41.51 m (136 ft 2 in)
Height	10.36 m (34 ft 0 in)	10.36 m (34 ft 0 in)
Max t/o weight	64 410 kg (142 000 lb)	76 655 kg (169 000 lb)
Max cruis. speed	974 km/h (605 mph)	953 km/h (592 mph)
Maximum range	4330 km (2690 miles)	3700 km (2300 miles)
Service ceiling	11 400 m (37 400 ft)	10 730 m (35 200 ft)

Opposite: **Aeronica** (RL)
Aeronica is Nicaragua's government-controlled national carrier. The company began operations on 1 November 1981, when it replaced the defunct Lanica. The carrier maintains scheduled international flights to Costa Rica, El Salvador, Mexico, Panama and the USA. It also provides domestic air links. With a base at Managua, Aeronica operates a fleet of Boeing 720, 727, CASA 212 Aviocar and DC-6 freighter aircraft. Jet services link Managua with Mexico City, San Salvador, San José and Panamá City. *(A J Mercer)*

Air Afrique (RK)

Air Afrique was officially formed in March 1961 by an agreement between 11 independent states which were formerly French colonies, and members of the Société pour le Développement du Transport Aérien en Afrique (Sodetraf). The countries involved were Cameroon, Central African Republic, Congo Brazzaville, Ivory Coast, Benin, Gabon, Upper Volta, Mauritania, Niger, Senegal, Chad and later Togo. Distribution of the shareholding changed with the withdrawal of Cameroon (in 1971) and Gabon (in 1976). Operations began in August 1961. The company currently provides internal services and routes cover 22 African states, together with international lines to Bordeaux, Paris, Nice, Lyons, Marseilles, Geneva, Zurich, Rome, Las Palmas, New York and Jeddah. A fleet of A300, DC-8, DC-10 and Boeing 727 equipment is used. The last named, YU-AKI, a Series 200, is leased from JAT, and can be seen here at Las Palmas in full Air Afrique colours.

(Udo and Birgit Schaefer Collection)

Air Algerie (AH)

Air Algérie, Algeria's national flag carrier since 1963, was formed in June 1953 following the merger of the original company with the same name, and Compagnie Air Transport. In 1972 the company became wholly government-owned. Today scheduled passenger and cargo services are operated to over 34 points in North and West Africa, France, Belgium, Spain, Italy, Greece, Austria, the United Kingdom, West Germany, Switzerland, Egypt, Yugoslavia, Bulgaria, the USSR, Libya, Romania, Czechoslovakia, and the Middle East. An extensive domestic network is operated in conjunction with Inter Air Services. Charter, air taxi and agricultural flights are also maintained. A fleet of A310, Boeing 727, 737, Hercules, Grumman Ag-Cat, F-27, Beech King and Queen Air, and Alouette aircraft is maintained. 7T-VEI, a Boeing 727-2D6 Advanced, is seen here taxiing at Algiers Airport. *(Udo and Birgit Schaefer Collection)*

Air Canada (AC)

Air Canada was founded in 1937 as Trans Canada Airlines. Operations began a year later between Vancouver and Seattle, with transcontinental passenger services commencing in April 1939. Today the company operates an extensive route network that covers the USA, Bahamas, Cuba, Europe, India and Singapore. As well as international flights, a domestic network in association with various commuter carriers is operated. Cargo services are also maintained across the network. With a base at Montreal, Air Canada operates a fleet of Boeing 727, 747, 767, DC-8, DC-9, and L-1011 Tristar equipment. This Boeing 727-200, C-GYNA, has fleet number 427, and is seen here just prior to take-off. *(Udo and Birgit Schaefer Collection)*

Air Charter (SF)

Air Charter was established in 1966 as Société Aérienne Française d'Affrètement. The company was formed as a wholly-owned subsidiary of Air France. In 1970, the carrier adopted the name Air Charter International. By 1984, Air Inter had been given a 20 per cent shareholding. This was granted in return for agreeing not to operate on the flag carrier's routes. During the same year, the airline changed to its current title. In early 1986, Air Charter was authorised to serve points in the French overseas territories, in competition with Air France's scheduled services. The company operates worldwide charters from over 33 domestic cities. Spain, Greece and Italy account for over half the passengers carried. A fleet of Boeing 727, 737 and SE-210 Caravelle aircraft is operated. F-GCMV, a 727-200, is seen here at Athens Airport, sporting the names of three airlines.
(R H Vandervord)

7

Opposite: **Air France** (AF)

Air France was founded on 30 August 1933, when Société Centrale pour L'Exploitation de Lignes Aériennes purchased the assets of Compagnie Générale Aéropostale. After World War II air transport was nationalised and Société Nationale Air France was set up on 1 January 1946. This was followed by Compagnie Nationale Air France on 16 June 1948, when the airline was incorporated by Act of Parliament. Today the company operates an extensive network of routes stretching worldwide. Air France serves cities throughout Europe, North Africa, the Middle East, North and South America, the Caribbean, Africa, Madagascar and the Indian Ocean, as well as to the Far East. The carrier has financial interests in Air Inter and Air Guadeloupe. Domestic services and routes to neighbouring countries, such as the UK, are contracted out to regional French airlines. Brit Air, for example, operates flights on behalf of Air France from Morlaix to London (Heathrow). An ATR-42-300 is utilised, sporting the national airline's livery. Air France operates a fleet of Airbus A300, A310, A320, Boeing 727, 737 and 747 aircraft. The company has an outstanding order for the Airbus A340. Boeing 727-200, F-BPJH, is seen here on approach to London (Heathrow).
(Udo and Birgit Schaefer Collection)

Above: **Air Jamaica** (JM)

Air Jamaica was formed in October 1968 by the Jamaican Government and Air Canada. Flight operations began on 1 April 1969 over a New York-Miami route. The carrier had succeeded Air Jamaica Ltd, a joint government venture with BOAC and BWIA, which had operated Kingston-New York services with leased aircraft since 1965. Today scheduled passenger and cargo services link the Jamaican capital and Montego Bay, with San Juan, Port-au-Prince, Grand Cayman, Miami, New York, Philadelphia, Baltimore, Atlanta, Los Angeles and Tampa. Direct services to London are maintained in conjunction with British Airways. The latter company's Boeing 747s are utilised. During the 1986-87 winter season, British Airways and Air Jamaica operated regular Concorde flights between Montego Bay and New York (as an extension of the New York-London service). A fleet of Airbus A300 and Boeing 727 aircraft is maintained by the Jamaican national carrier. VR-CMD, a 727-200, is seen here at Kingston. *(N Chalcraft)*

Air Mali (MY)

Air Mali was formed in October 1960, as the national airline of the Republic of Mali. Operations began in 1961 with technical and equipment assistance being supplied by Aeroflot. The company was aided by a gift from the British Government of three ex-BEA DC-3s. Scheduled passenger services are operated to various domestic points, as well as international cities in France, Ivory Coast, Nigeria, Algeria, Morocco and the Congo Republic. Air Mali operates a fleet of Il-18, Boeing 727, 737, An-24, DHC-6 and BAe 146 aircraft. The company's sole 727-100C, TZ-ADR, is seen here at Stansted. *(P Bish)*

Air Nauru (ON)

Air Nauru, the government-owned airline of the island republic of Nauru, was formed in 1970 as a division of the Directorate of Civil Aviation, within the Ministry of Island Development & Industry. Operations began on 14 February of that year with an experimental service between Nauru and Brisbane, using a Dassault Falcon. Today scheduled passenger and cargo operations link the island with Apia, Auckland, Guam, Hong Kong, Honiara, Kagoshima, Koror, Manila, Melbourne, Nadi, Niue, Noumea, Okinawa, Pago Pago, Port Vila, Rarotonga, Sydney and Tarawa. A fleet of Boeing 737s and a sole 727 aircraft is utilised. C2-RN5, a Boeing 727-100, although no longer operated by Air Nauru, was purchased in December 1977. It is pictured here at Yaren Airport, Nauru, in March 1985. *(Udo and Birgit Schaefer Collection)*

11

Air Panama (OP)

Air Panama was formed in August 1967 with the assistance of the Spanish national airline, Iberia. Operations began in 1969 using a leased DC-9-15, with services from a base at Panama City. Today the airline utilises two Boeing 727s and a DC-10.

Scheduled passenger services are maintained from Panama City to Bogota, Caracas, Guayaquil, Lima, Mexico City and Miami. The Panamanian national flag carrier employs nearly 200 people. HP-619, a Boeing 727-81, is seen here at Miami Airport on 17 November 1983. (A J Mercer)

Alitalia (AZ)

Alitalia was formed in September 1946 following co-operation with BEA. Operations began in May 1947 over a domestic network, using Fiat G.12s, Savoia-Marchetti SM.95s and Lancastrians. The present name was adopted in 1957 when, with the backing of IRI, the two major Italian airlines, Alitalia and LAI, merged. Today the company operates a worldwide network of scheduled passenger and cargo services from Italy to points in Europe, Africa, North and South America, the Middle and Far East, and Australia. In October 1986, Lima (Peru) was added to the network. In July of that year, Alitalia and CAAC joined forces to operate a combined Beijing-Rome (via Sharjah) service, initially utilising the Chinese company's aircraft. However in 1987 this changed and both carriers operate alternate services with their Boeing 747s. Alitalia utilises a fleet of A300, Boeing 747, DC-9, ATR-42, MD-82, Piaggio PI66-DL3, and SIAI Marchetti SF.260 aircraft. The company has an outstanding order for a number of MD-11 types. Although the type is no longer operated, a Boeing 727-200, I-DIRU, is seen here at London (Heathrow).
(Udo and Birgit Schaefer Collection)

13

Below: **American Airlines** (AA)
American Airlines was formed on 13 May 1934 as a direct successor to American Airways. Since the company's formation the carrier has played a vital role as a launch customer in the development of many civil aircraft. These include the Douglas DC-3, DC-7, CV-240, CV-990, Lockheed Electra and DC-10. America's huge route system extends from Bermuda to Hawaii, from Montreal and Toronto in the north, Acapulco and Mexico City in the south and across the Atlantic to Europe. The airline flies over 25 million people annually across its network, and with a fleet that is continually expanding it is hardly surprising that the company ranks amongst the largest aviation operators in the world. A fleet of Boeing 727, 737, 767, MD-82, DC-10, BAe 146 and Airbus A300 types is operated. American also owns Air Cal, a West Coast regional operator. N872AA, a Boeing 727-200, is seen here at San Francisco on 21 June 1980. *(A J Mercer)*

Opposite: **Avianca** (AV)
Avianca, one of the world's oldest airlines, can trace its history as far back as December 1919, with the formation of Sociedad Colombia-Alemana de Transportes Aereos. It was the first airline in the Americas, and was formed by a group of German settlers. Scheduled operations began two years later between Girardot and Barranquilla, using a fleet of Junkers F-13 floatplanes. Today the company provides an extensive network of operations that covers South America, the USA, Spain, France and West Germany. A fleet of Boeing 707, 727 and 747 aircraft is utilised. Boeing 727-259 Advanced, N203AV, is seen arriving at Miami Airport on 21 November 1983. *(A J Mercer)*

Opposite: **Aviateca Guatemala** (GU)
Aviateca was established in March 1945 as Aviateca Empresa Guatemalteca de Aviacion SA. It was formed to succeed the company owned by Pan American Airways as the Guatemalan national carrier. Aviateca currently operates regional services in Central America, serving Merida and Mexico City, as well as Houston, Miami and New Orleans in the USA. The company operates two Boeing 727s and has suspended all but one domestic service, this being to Flores in the low-lying Pete region in the north of the country. This is the only airport in the area which has a paved runway capable of handling jet equipment. TG-ALA, a Boeing 727-25C, is seen here just prior to touchdown at Miami Airport. *(A J Mercer)*

Above: **Aviogenex** (JJ)
Aviogenex was formed in 1968 as Genex Airlines. Flight activites began on 30 March 1969 with two Tu-134 jetliners, operating flights between Dusseldorf and Belgrade. The company is the air transport division of Generalexport, one of Yugoslavia's largest government-controlled trading firms. The airline operates international passenger tour charters, primarily to Europe, and also cargo flights to Europe, the Middle East, and Africa. Aviogenex maintains a fleet of Boeing 727, 737 and Tu-134A aircraft. Boeing 727-200, YU-AKM, is seen here at Gatwick Airport.
(Udo and Birgit Schaefer Collection)

Boeing 727-200

The Boeing 727-200 "Long Body" was announced for the first time on 5 August 1965. An order was shortly afterwards placed by Northeast Airlines. Deliveries of the aircraft began on 11 December 1967. The aircraft, and its variants, proved to be the most popular commercial aircraft of all, with a total of 1832 units being built. N1787B, the 727-200 prototype, can be seen here on its first flight. *(Boeing Commercial Airplane Company)*

Braniff Airways (BN)

Braniff Airways, a Dallas-based US major airline, was founded by two brothers, Paul and Tom Braniff, in 1928. Due to serious financial difficulties, the company was forced to shut down on 12 May 1982. However, Braniff was able to recommence tailored-down operations in March 1984. Financial backing was given from Hyatt Inc. Braniff operates a hub-and-spoke network of scheduled passenger services from Dallas/Fort Worth, to Boston, Chicago, Denver, Kansas City, Las Vegas, Phoenix, New York, San Francisco, and Washington DC. A fleet of Boeing 727-200 aircraft is maintained. N462BN is seen here at 'base' airport. *(Udo and Birgit Schaefer Collection)*

Cayman Airways (KX)

Cayman Airways was formed in July 1968 to replace Cayman Brac Airways, the subsidiary of the Costa Rican airline, LACSA. The original shareholders of the company were LACSA and the Cayman Island Government. However, in December 1977, the airline became wholly-government owned. A scheduled route network links George Town (Grand Cayman) with Jamaica and the USA.

Domestic services are provided to Little Cayman and Cayman Brac. Passenger charter flights are operated to Atlanta, Baltimore, New York, Detroit, Philadelphia, St Louis, Boston and Tampa. A Boeing 727, Shorts 330 and Trislander fleet is maintained. However, during 1987, a Boeing 737 was leased. N272AF, a 727-200, is seen here sporting the Cayman livery. *(K Armes)*

Condor Flugdienst (DF)
Condor is a wholly-owned subsidiary of Lufthansa. The company was formed in 1961 by the merger of Deutsche Flugdienst (founded in 1955 as a Lufthansa subsidiary) and Condor Luftreederei (founded in 1957 and acquired by Lufthansa in 1959). The carrier concentrates on charter and inclusive-tour operations to destinations in the Mediterranean, the Canary Islands, Africa, Far East and North America. The fleet consists of A300, A310, DC-10, Boeing 727 and 737 types. D-ABMI, a 727-200, is seen here at Athens Airport in June 1985.
(R Vandervord)

Opposite: **Copa** (CM)

Copa was founded on 15 August 1947, with assistance from Pan Am. Domestic operations began that same year with a service between Panama City and David. International destinations were added in 1965, and in 1971 Pan Am withdrew financial support. The company today operates international services to Colombia, Costa Rica, El Salvador, Guatemala, Nicaragua, Jamaica and Haiti, as well as the Dominican Republic. Copa operates a fleet of Boeing 727 and Electra aircraft. HP-1063 is seen here at Kingston. *(N Mills)*

Below: **Continental Airlines** (CO)

Continental Airlines is owned by Texas Air Cor- poration. It can trace its history back to July 1934, when the company began services as Varney Speed Lines. In May 1937 the carrier purchased the Denver-Pueblo route of Wyoming Air Service and moved to a Denver headquarters. Later that year the present title was adopted. Development continued for a number of years until the 1955 award of the Chicago-Los Angeles route (via Kansas City and Denver) marked the company's full transition to a main line trunk carrier. In October 1981 Texas Air acquired a controlling interest in the company, and a year later the two companies began operating as a single carrier, under the name of Continental. In September 1983 the company filed for Chapter 11 bankruptcy. This involved reducing its routes from 78 to 25, and its workforce dropped from 12 000 to 4200. In September 1985, Continental filed a plan of reorganisation with the US Bankruptcy Court, and a year later emerged from its Chapter 11 protection. Today the company operates a fleet that consists of Boeing 727, 737, 747, DC-9, DC-10, A300 and MD-82 aircraft. A route structure now covers the USA, Mexico, Canada, Australia, New Zealand and the UK. In June 1986, Continental signed marketing agreements with several com- panies to form a feeder subsidiary called 'Con- tinental Express'. Boeing 727-200, N88705, is seen here prior to take-off.

(Udo and Birgit Schaefer Collection)

Dan Air Services (DA)

Dan Air was founded in May 1953 as a subsidiary of Davies & Newman Holdings Plc, from which its name is derived. The company has developed extensive inclusive-tour charter operations from most major UK cities as well as Berlin, and a growing scheduled network of services. Dan Air operates domestic flights to and from destinations that include London (Heathrow and Gatwick), Newcastle, Inverness, Bristol, Cardiff, Leeds/ Bradford, Belfast, Aberdeen, Bournemouth and Jersey. International services are operated to Innsbruck, Amsterdam, Bergen, Stavanger, Oslo and Lourdes, as well as many other destinations. A fleet of A300, Boeing 727, 737, BAe 146, BAe 748 and BAe 1-11 aircraft is maintained. In 1986 Dan Air carried more passengers than any other UK independent airline. G-BHNF, a 727-200, is seen here taxiing at Gatwick on 11 January 1981. *(A J Mercer)*

Delta Air Lines (DL)

Delta Air Lines was founded in 1924 as the world's first crop dusting company, and commercial passenger services began in 1929. In 1953 the carrier merged with Chicago and Southern Air Lines, and in 1972 it absorbed Northwest Airlines. Today Delta operates a vast route network that covers the entire mainland USA and Hawaii, as well as points in Canada, Bermuda, Bahamas, Puerto Rico, the UK, France and West Germany. In April 1987, Delta took over Western Airlines and has become one of the USA's largest companies. A combined fleet comprises Boeing 727-200, Boeing 737-200, 737-300, 767-200, 767-300, DC-8, DC-9, DC-10, and L-1011 aircraft. A Boeing 727-200, N405DA, is seen here at Atlanta. *(K Armes)*

Dominicana (DO)

Dominicana was founded in 1944 by a group of businessmen, headed by Guillermo Santoni Calero, and Pan American World Airways. The company operates scheduled passenger jet services between the Dominican Republic and Haiti, the Netherlands Antilles, Puerto Rico, the USA and Venezuela. A fleet of Boeing 707, 727 and DC-6B aircraft is maintained. Boeing 727-100C, HI-212, is seen here prior to arrival at Miami. *(P Hornfeck)*

26

Eastern Air Lines (EA)

Eastern Air Lines commenced operations in May 1928 when Pitcairn Aviation initiated a mail service between New York and Atlanta. The following year, the company was acquired by North American Aviation and changed its name to Eastern Air Transport. The present name was adopted in 1938, following an extensive reorganisation. Today, Eastern operates a vast network of scheduled services to over 100 cities in the USA, Bermuda, Canada, the Bahamas, the Caribbean and South America. The company was the pioneer of the 'Air Shuttle'. The services between New York, Washington and Boston offer a no-reservation, guaranteed-seat operation, which was inaugurated back in April 1961. In 1986 the airline became part of the vast Texas Air Corporation, although Eastern still retains its separate identity. A fleet of A300, Boeing 727, 757, L-1011, and DC-9 aircraft is maintained. In addition the airline operates various turbo-props in a subsidiary called 'Eastern Express'. This is made up of various third level companies that feed passengers out to the smaller communities. N810EA, a Boeing 727-200, is seen here arriving at Miami on 21 November 1983. *(A J Mercer)*

Europe Aero Service (EY)

Europe Aéro Service was formed in July 1965 as a subsidiary of Société Aéro Sahara. Scheduled operations began a year later with a service between Perpignan and Palma. Today the company operates passenger and cargo flights from Nîmes to Carcassonne, Perpignan, Ajaccio, Bastia, Palma and Ibiza; also Paris to Valence; and Perpignan to Palma and Toulouse. The airline also operates services on behalf of the French airline, Air Inter, as well as undertaking charter and inclusive tour flights. A fleet of Sud-Est Caravelle 10Bs and a sole Boeing 727-200 aircraft is operated. The latter, F-GCGQ, can be seen outside the company's hangars at Perpignan.

(Udo and Birgit Schaefer Collection)

Evergreen International Airlines (EZ)
Evergreen was established in 1975 after Evergreen Helicopters acquired Johnson International Airlines, of Missoula, Montana. The company can trace its history as far back as 1924, when Johnson Flying Service was formed. Evergreen maintains scheduled domestic freight flights, as well as world-wide cargo charter and contract services. Points flown to include Seattle, Portland, San Francisco, Los Angeles, Chicago, Dallas/Fort Worth, Boston, New York, Atlanta and Vancouver. A fleet of DC-8, DC-9, Boeing 727, L-188 Electra, and Falcon 20F aircraft is maintained. N725EV, a 727-100C, is seen here. *(Udo and Birgit Schaefer Collection)*

Federal Express (FM)

Federal Express was formed by F W Smith in 1971. Operations began in April 1973 using Falcon 20 business jets. Following CAB deregulation of air cargo in November 1977, authority to operate larger aircraft was received, and a fleet of Boeing 727, 737 and DC-10 aircraft was assembled. The 737 and Falcon types have now been phased out of service. An operations base is maintained at Memphis International Airport, from which an extensive network of nightly jet cargo flights filter out to every major city in the USA and Canada. The company offers a two-day service to Europe, and a three-day service to Tokyo, Hong Kong, and Singapore. Documents and packages not exceeding 69 kg (150 lb) in weight or 330 cm (130 in) in length and girth combined are carried. Latest additions to the Federal fleet include over 100 Caravan 208A and 208B aircraft. The airline has ordered a quantity of the 'all-new' MD-11 for delivery in the 1990s. N119FE, a Boeing 727-25C, is seen here wearing the company's striking livery.

(Udo and Birgit Schaefer Collection)

Flying Tiger Line (FT)

Flying Tiger was formed on 25 June 1945 as National Skyway Freight. Initial activities were restricted to charter flights with a fleet of 8 Budd Conestoga aircraft. In 1947 the company adopted its present title, and two years later inaugurated domestic cargo services. Trans-Pacific international services were launched in 1969, and in 1980 Flying Tiger acquired Seaboard World Airlines. Today Tiger is the world's largest cargo airline and operates a huge domestic network. Flights are also maintained to the Caribbean, South America, Europe and the Middle East. A fleet of DC-8, Boeing 727 and 747 aircraft is operated. 727-100C, N1933, is seen here. *(N Mills)*

Hapag Lloyd Flug (HF)

Hapag Lloyd was formed in July 1972 as Hapag Lloyd Flugzeug, with operations beginning the following year. The company, which is part of the Hapag Lloyd Shipping Group, was given authority to merge with Bavaria Germanair in January 1979. Today the company operates passenger charter and inclusive tour flights to the Canary Islands, Central, Southern and Eastern Europe, as well as West Africa. An all-jet fleet of A300, A310, Boeing 727 and 737-400 aircraft is maintained. D-AHLR, a Boeing 727-89, is seen here at Frankfurt on 4 August 1979. This aircraft was subsequently sold in 1983 to Scribe Air, as 9Q-CBT. *(A J Mercer)*

Iberia (IB)

Iberia, Spain's national flag carrier, was formed in 1927. The company was given exclusive rights to operate the country's air services. Initial shareholding was split between the government, Deutsche Luft Hansa, and other local interests. Iberia opened a service to London in May 1946, closely followed by routes to Central and South America. Today the company operates a scheduled network of passenger and cargo flights to the Americas, Africa and Europe. In May 1986, Iberia launched services to Tokyo, its first Far East destination. The company operates a fleet of A300, Boeing 727, DC-9, DC-10, and Boeing 747 aircraft. The carrier has interests in the Spanish domestic carrier, Aviaco. EC-DDZ, a 727-200, is seen here at Madrid. *(DPR Marketing & Sales)*

Above: **Icelandair** (FI)

Icelandair was set up in its present form on 1 August 1973, as the holding company for Flugfelag Islands (the original Icelandair, formed in 1937), and Loftleidir (Icelandic Airlines, formed in 1944). The company assumed all operating responsibilities in October 1979. Icelandair is famous for its low-cost international services, and has in recent years been Europe's fastest-growing carrier. The airline's shareholders now number 3594 and the company is 100 per cent privately owned. Scheduled passenger and cargo services link Reykjavik with New York (JFK), Chicago, Washington/Baltimore, Detroit, Orlando, Paris, London (Heathrow), Glasgow, Oslo, Stockholm, Gothenburg, Bergen, Copenhagen, Frankfurt, Salzburg, Luxembourg and the Faroe Islands, as well as Kulusuk and Narssarssuaq in Greenland. Icelandair also operates to 11 domestic points, as well as maintaining international and regional charter services. A fleet of DC-8, F-27 and Boeing 727 aircraft is maintained. Seen here at Reykjavik, TF-FLI, a 727-200, is awaiting passengers for a flight to London. *(Udo and Birgit Schaefer Collection)*

Opposite: **Independent Air**

Independent Air is a Georgia-based charter company which operates domestic and international services. The airline also maintains the Atlanta Skylarks air travel club. The carrier began commercial contract services in July 1966, and gained final charter airline certification in August 1984. A fleet of Boeing 707, 720, and 727 aircraft is maintained. N154FN, its sole 727-100, is seen here. *(N Mills)*

Iran Air (IA)

Iran Air, the government-controlled Iranian national airline, maintains scheduled jet services within Iran and to various destinations in southern and eastern Asia, the Middle East, and Europe. The company was established in 1962 following a merger of Persian Air Services and Iranian Airlines. Since the rise to power of Ayatollah Khomeini in 1979, the operations of Iran Air have been dramatically curtailed. Prior to the fall of the Shah, the company had been operating to 29 destin- ations, ranging as far west as New York, and as far east as Tokyo. There were over 100 scheduled weekly departures. At one stage there was hope that Iran Air might operate Concorde, and it was the final company to withdraw from its contract, with the exception of the current two operators. In 1987, less than 30 weekly flights depart Tehran for the company's overseas destinations. A fleet of A300, Boeing 707, 727, 737, and 747 aircraft is maintained. Boeing 727-100, EP-IRC, is seen here. *(Udo and Birgit Schaefer Collection)*

Iraqi Airways (IA)

Iraqi Airways was founded in December 1945 by Iraqi State Railways. An inaugural service was operated a month later, between Baghdad and Basra, using de Havilland Rapides. International lines were opened approximately six months later. Today these serve Europe, the Middle East, the USSR, India, Pakistan and the Far East. A long haul route between Rio de Janeiro and Baghdad, via Amman and Lisbon, is operated in conjunction with Royal Jordanian Airlines. Domestic services are maintained, although intermittently, due to the present conflict between Iraq and Iran. A fleet of An-12, An-24, Boeing 707, 727, 737, 747, and Il-76 aircraft are operated. Two Tu-124s are amongst the fleet, although these are utilised on VIP flights along with Dassault Falcon and Jetstar II types. YI-AGQ, a Boeing 727-200, is seen here at Amsterdam's Schiphol Airport.
(Udo and Birgit Schaefer Collection)

37

Below: **Kabo Air**
Kabo Air was established in 1975, and operated its first Hadj charter flight from Maiduguri, Nigeria, in 1980. Charter airline rights were obtained in 1982. The privately-owned carrier operates regular flights between the Nigerian cities of Kano, Lagos, Port Harcourt and Kaduna. International services are operated to other African countries, the Middle East and Europe. Kabo Air is a major organiser of Hadj trips to Mecca, and it regularly leases Boeing 747s and other aircraft to transport Hadj pilgrims to Jeddah. A fleet of Boeing 727, 737 and Caravelle aircraft is maintained.
(Udo and Birgit Schaefer Collection)

Lacsa (LR)

Lacsa was designated as the Costa Rican flag carrier in 1949. The company was originally formed in Decémber 1945 by Pan American Airways. In June of the following year, operations began using DC-3 equipment over a domestic network. Today Lacsa operates regional passenger and cargo services from a base at San José's Santamaria International Airport to San Salvador, Panama City, Mexico City and Cancun. Points also served include Guatemala City, San Pedro Sula, Miami, New Orleans, Los Angeles, Cartagena, Baranquilla, Caracas and Maracaibo. The airline operates a fleet of Boeing 727 and DC-8 equipment. TI-LRQ, a 727-200, is seen here landing at Miami on 21 November 1983. *(A J Mercer)*

Lufthansa (LH)

Lufthansa, the West German national airline, operates scheduled jet services over a vast intercontinental route system that connects nine domestic and 118 foreign points. It was established in 1926 when Deutsche Luft Hansa was formed through the merger of Aero Lloyd and Junkers Luftverkehr. Following World War II, the company was dissolved. A new West German national airline known as Luftag was established in 1953, being renamed Deutsche Lufthansa a year later. The airline operates a large fleet of aircraft that includes the Boeing 727. The aircraft are used on internal and European routes, the latter including Cologne-London (Heathrow).

(Udo and Birgit Schaefer Collection)

Mexicana (MX)

Mexicana was formed in 1921 and began operations on 12 July of that year. The airline's first contract was the carriage of freight to the oil fields around Tampico, using Lincoln Standard and Fairchild biplanes. Scheduled services were not added until 1928, when a line between Mexico City and Tampico via Tuxpam was opened. Today, scheduled passenger and cargo services link the Mexican capital with the USA, Puerto Rico, Costa Rica, Cuba and Guatemala City. During 1982 the Mexican Government took a 58 per cent controlling interest in the company. A fleet of Boeing 727-200 Advanced and DC-10-15 equipment is maintained. XA-DUI is seen here landing at Miami during November 1983. (A J Mercer)

Olympic Airways (OA)

Olympic Airways was formed on 1 January 1957, when Aristotle Onassis, a Greek shipowner, acquired the entire assets of TAE, the then Greek national airline. Today extensive scheduled passenger and cargo services link Athens with most European capitals. International destinations include Montreal, New York, Johannesburg, Benghazi, Nairobi, Cairo, Abu Dhabi, Sydney and Melbourne. A comprehensive domestic network covers the Greek islands and points on the mainland. Olympic Aviation, a light aircraft company responsible for charter and air taxi operations, as well as air training, is a subsidiary of the national airline. A fleet of A300, Boeing 707, 727, 737 and 747 aircraft is maintained. SX-CBB, a 727-200, is seen here at Geneva. *(A J Mercer)*

Pan American World Airways (PA)

Pan Am inaugurated a regular mail service between Key West and Havana on 28 October 1927. Passenger flights commenced over the same line in January of the following year. Early in the 1930s, routes were operated to Central and South America, the Caribbean and Mexico. In 1932 the company formed an Alaskan division. By October 1936, trans-Pacific passenger flights had commenced, followed by Europe in 1939, and to Africa in 1940. American Overseas Airways, a major Atlantic competitor, was taken over in 1950. In the ensuing decades, Pan Am has become one of the best-known names in aviation history. The airline played a vital role in commercial jet transport when, in 1955, it placed orders for 20 Boeing 707s and 25 DC-8s. The carrier was also the first company to operate the Boeing 747, when it did so in 1970. Today Pan Am operates a route network of over 403 000 km (250 000 miles), linking over 100 points in 50 nations. It has a headquarters in New York, although it bases its aircraft throughout the world. A fleet of A300, A310, Boeing 727, 737 and 747 aircraft is maintained. Some 16 A320s are on order for 1988 delivery. N550PS, a 727-200, is seen here. *(Udo and Birgit Schaefer Collection)*

Piedmont Airlines (PI)

Piedmont Airlines was formed in 1940 as an aircraft sales and service operator. Flights began on 1 January 1948 with scheduled services between Wilmington and Cincinnati, using Douglas DC-3 aircraft. Extensions through North Carolina, Kentucky and Virginia were later added. Today the company serves over 113 cities in 27 states, as well as to Canada. Major hubs are located at Charlotte's Douglas International, Dayton, and Baltimore airports. Piedmont purchased Henson Airlines in 1983, with Empire Airlines being acquired in 1986. These latter companies operate under the 'Piedmont Regional' banner. The company owns the largest Boeing 737 fleet in the world, operating both the -200 and -300 models. It also became the launch customer for the larger -400 variant. A fleet of Boeing 727, 767 and F-28 types is also operated. N558PS, a Boeing 727-200, is seen here in full Piedmont colours. During 1987 USAir took over the company. It was understood that Piedmont would retain its identity for a few more months. On 15 June 1987, the company inaugurated transatlantic flights between Tampa, Florida and London (Gatwick). The service is flown via Charlotte, using Boeing 767-200ER aircraft.

(Udo and Birgit Schaefer Collection)

Skyworld (PC)

Skyworld is a Denver-based travel club providing domestic and worldwide international services for nearly 68 000 members. The club was established in 1966 as Ports Of Call — Denver. Skyworld also undertakes contract jet flights and has obtained certification as a charter airline. The company operates a Boeing 707 and 727 fleet. Its sole example of the Boeing 727-100, N721PC, is seen here at Denver. The current name was adopted in 1987. *(Udo and Birgit Schaefer Collection)*

Royal Air Maroc (AT)

Royal Air Maroc was formed in 1953 as Compagnie Cherifienne de Transports Aériens. This was a result of a merger involving Air Atlas and Air Maroc. The airline became the national flag carrier of newly-independent Morocco on 28 June 1957. RAM ownership is controlled by the government, Air France and private interests. The company has financial holdings in Royal Air Inter. Today scheduled passenger and cargo services are operated from a base at Casablanca, to points in Morocco, North and West Africa, Europe, the Middle East, New York, and Montreal, as well as to Rio de Janeiro. A fleet of Boeing 707, 727, 737, 747 and 757 aircraft is operated. CN-CCF, a 727-200, is seen here at London (Heathrow) Airport. (P Hornfeck)

Opposite: **Royal Jordanian Airline** (RJ)
Formerly known as Alia, Royal Jordanian was established in December 1963. It was formed as a successor to Jordan Airways. Flight activities began that same month with DC-7 and Herald aircraft. A small network of routes then linked Amman with Beirut, Cairo, Jeddah, Jerusalem and Kuwait. The Jordanian Government took over control of Alia in 1968, and in the last decade the company has become one of the largest carriers in the Middle East. Royal Jordanian's holdings include a 64 per cent interest in Arab Wings, a 50 per cent interest in Arab Air Cargo, and a 20 per cent share in Sierra Leone Airways; as well as additional interests in travel, hotel and aviation maintenance

companies. The airline operates scheduled passenger and cargo services throughout the Middle East, as well as maintaining flights to Europe, North America, and the Philippines. A fleet of Boeing 707, 727, 747, Tristar and A310 aircraft is maintained. Royal Jordanian has also ordered the A320 to replace its 727 fleet. An example of the latter type is seen here on approach to Heathrow Airport. It is sporting the company's old livery. *(P Hornfeck)*

Above: **Royal Nepal Airlines** (RA)
The airline was established by the Government of Nepal on 1 July 1958 to take over all domestic routes, together with the international routes between India and Nepal, previously operated by

Indian Airlines. Royal Nepal Airlines became launch customer for the Boeing 757-200 Combi in February 1986, when it announced an order for a single unit. Current operations include scheduled passenger and freight services linking Kathmandu with 37 domestic points. International routes are open to Bangkok, Dhaka, Dubai, Hong Kong, Delhi, Calcutta, Karachi, Colombo, Singapore and Rangoon. A fleet of Boeing 727, 757, BAe 748, DHC-6 and Pilatus PC-6 aircraft is operated. 9N-ABD, a 727-100, is seen here at Cologne, sporting the company's new livery.
(Udo and Birgit Schaefer Collection)

49

Sahsa (SH)

Sahsa was established in 1944 and began flight activities in October 1945. The company is a major Central American airline and operates scheduled flights over domestic routes in Honduras, as well as along international lines to Belize, Costa Rica, El Salvador, Guatemala, Nicaragua, Panama and the USA. Sahsa is jointly owned by private Honduran interests and TAN Airlines. The carrier has a majority sharehold in the Honduran domestic operator, Anhsa. It is with this airline that it co-ordinates certain local services. A fleet of Boeing 727, 737, and DC-3 aircraft is maintained. HR-SHE, a 727-100, is seen here at Miami.
(N Chalcraft)

SAT Fluggesellschaft (JO)

SAT operated international passenger charters for the major West German tour operators until its routes and assets were taken over by Germania Fluggesellschaft during 1986. Destinations were primarily served within Europe, the Mediterranean, North Africa, and the Canary Islands, as well as the Near East. SAT was formed in April 1978, with operations commencing in September of that year, using a Fokker F-27 Friendship. Until its demise the airline operated Sud-Est Caravelle 10R and Boeing 727-81 and -89 types. D-AHLS, the latter model, is seen here at Köln/Bonn Airport.
(Udo and Birgit Schaefer Collection)

Southwest Airlines (WN)

Southwest Airlines, a Dallas-based carrier, operates high-frequency, low-fare interstate services connecting over 11 destinations in Texas with New Orleans, Oklahoma City, Tulsa, Albuquerque, Phoenix, Las Vegas, San Diego, Los Angeles, San Francisco, Ontario, Kansas City, St Louis, Denver, Little Rock and Chicago. The airline was formed in March 1967 under the name Air Southwest. The present name was adopted in June 1971, when operations began using three Boeing 737-200s. In December 1978 Southwest was certified as an interstate carrier, obtaining permission to extend service to New Orleans. In June 1985, Southwest acquired TranStar Airlines. An all-Boeing 737 fleet is now maintained. Until recently, Boeing 727-200 aircraft were utilised. N564PE is seen here at Dallas Love Field. *(Udo and Birgit Schaefer Collection)*

TAME (EQ)

TAME was formed on 17 December 1962 as an air force transport division. It began operations with Douglas DC-3 aircraft. Destinations initially served included Quito, Ibarra, Riobamba and Tulcan. A governmental decree legally created the airline as Transportes Aereos Militares Ecuatorianos on 20 May 1964. The company, a domestic commercial airline operated by the Ecuadorian Air Force, provides scheduled passenger services to over 12 destinations. A fleet of Boeing 727, F-28, L-188 Electra and DHC-6 Twin Otter aircraft is operated. HC-BLV, a 727-100 seen here wearing the registration G-BKCG, was at the time on a lease to Dan Air. *(P Hornfeck)*

Opposite: **TAP Air Portugal** (TP)
TAP, the Portuguese national flag carrier, was formed in March 1945 as a division of Civil Aeronautics Secretariat. Services began in September of the following year, with a flight to Madrid, extending shortly after to Angola and Mozambique. Since 1967, TAP has been operating an all-jet fleet over an extensive international network that covers North and South America, Europe and Africa. On a domestic basis the airline links Lisbon with Madeira, Las Palmas on the Canary Islands, and São Miguel and Teraira in the Azores. On the mainland, services link Lisbon with the rest of Portugal. A fleet of Boeing 727, 737 and L-1011 Tristar aircraft is operated. The company has an outstanding order for the A310-300, which will be delivered from 1988 onwards. CS-TBQ, a Boeing 727-172C, is seen here at Geneva on 19 March 1983. This aircraft has now left the TAP fleet and is currently with Purolator Courier. *(A J Mercer)*

Above: **Transbrasil** (QD)
Transbrasil was formed on 5 January 1955 as Sadia SA Transportes Aereas. Its aim was to carry fresh meat products from Concordia to the markets of São Paulo, using a DC-3. Scheduled passenger services over that same routeing and from other points in the state of Santa Catarina were started in March 1956. The present name was adopted in 1972. Transbrasil operates an extensive domestic passenger and cargo network linking such points as Rio, Manaus, Recife, Vitoria, Campinas and Natal. A fleet of Boeing aircraft is operated, from the 707 through to the wide-body 767. A Boeing 727-27 is seen here. *(Udo and Birgit Schaefer Collection)*

Tunis Air (TU)

Tunis Air was founded in 1948 by the Tunisian Government, which has a 51 per cent shareholding. Air France holds 15 per cent, whilst other interests hold the remainder. Passenger and cargo services are operated to Europe, the Middle East and Africa from a base at Tunis. Domestic operations link the towns of Jerba, Monastir, Tozeur and Sfax with the capital. A fleet of A300, Boeing 727 and 737 aircraft are operated. TS-JHV, a 727-200 Advanced, is seen here at Tunis.
(Udo and Birgit Schaefer Collection)

Turk Hava Yollari (TK)

THY was formed by the Turkish Government in May 1933 as Devlet Hava Yollari. The present title was adopted in 1956, when the airline became a corporation. The company operates scheduled passenger and cargo services from Ankara, Istanbul, Antalya, Izmir and Adana to 11 other domestic points. International lines are serviced throughout Europe, the Middle East, Libya, India, Singapore and Pakistan. Charter flights are also operated to the Federal Republic of Germany. A fleet of DC-9, DC-10, Boeing 707, 727, and A310 aircraft is operated. Boeing 727-200, TC-JBG, is seen here at Antalya. *(Udo and Birgit Schaefer Collection)*

United Airlines (UA)

United Airlines is one of the largest airlines in the world, as measured by operating revenue passenger-miles flown. The company serves over 100 cities throughout the USA, Canada, Bahamas, Mexico, Japan and Hong Kong. United was formed in 1926 as Varney Air Lines. It was later organised as a management company for Varney, Boeing Air Transport, Pacific Air Transport and National Air Transport, with the current name being adopted in 1931. A fleet of Boeing 727, 737, 747, 767, DC-8, L-1011 Tristar and DC-10 aircraft is maintained. N7624U, a Boeing 727-200, is seen here at Seattle/Tacoma Airport on 19 June 1980. *(A J Mercer)*

United Parcel Service Company

UPS was initially in the air express business from 1929 to 1931 on the US West Coast. In 1953 the company started a two-day 'UPS-AIR' service (now called 'UPS 2nd Day Air') between major American cities. In 1982 the carrier entered the overnight market and now claims to serve more US points than any other carrier. By 1985 UPS had initiated its European services. Today the company provides a scheduled network of parcel services throughout the USA and Europe. The services offered are 'UPS Next Day Air' (to every address in the 48 contiguous states, Hawaii and Puerto Rico), and 'UPS 2nd Day Air' (same territory, plus Anchorage in Alaska). There is also 'UPS International Service'. A fleet of Boeing 727, 747, 757PF, DC-8 and various turbo-prop aircraft is utilised. N922UP, a 727-100, is seen here.
(Udo and Birgit Schaefer Collection)

USAir (AL)

USAir was formed in 1937 as All America Airways, adopting the name 'Allegheny Airlines' in 1953. Operations began in September of that year with a unique 'Pick-up' mail service. Stinson Reliant aircraft were used over a network of routes radiating from Pittsburgh. In July 1968, Lake Central Airlines was acquired, followed by Mohawk Airlines in April 1972. In 1986, USAir purchased Suburban Airlines, followed by PSA and Piedmont in 1987. The airline provides scheduled passenger services to over 100 cities in almost every US state. A number of smaller carriers operate Allegheny Commuter flights; these connect with main line USAir services at major points. A fleet of Boeing 727, 737, BAe 1-11, F-28, Fokker 100, DC-9, MD-80, BAe 146, and Boeing 767 aircraft is operated. *(DPR Marketing & Sales)*

Western Air Lines (WA)

On 1 April 1987, Western Air Lines became a fully-owned subsidiary of Delta Air Lines. The company can trace its history as far back as July 1925, to the foundation of Western Air Express. An inaugural flight over a Los Angeles-Salt Lake City route was made on 17 April 1926, using Douglas M-2s. Prior to the merger, Western operated a vast network of scheduled passenger services over the western states. Destinations included Fairbanks and Anchorage (Alaska), Vancouver and Edmonton (Canada), Honolulu (Hawaii), Acapulco, Mexico City (Mexico), Washington DC and New York City. A fleet of Boeing 727, 737, and DC-10 aircraft was operated. N2814W, a 727-200 Advanced, is seen here at San Francisco, on 23 June 1980.
(A J Mercer)

World Airways (WO)

World Airways was formed in 1948 to operate charter services. In 1950 the company was purchased by E J Daly, who held 81 per cent of the shareholding until he died in January 1984. Following CAB approval in early 1979, World commenced scheduled low-fare trans-continental services that linked New York (Newark) and Baltimore/Washington DC with Los Angeles and Oakland. Flights commenced on 12 April of that year. In September 1986, the company shut down its entire scheduled operations network, which accounted for the bulk of services, and decided to concentrate on charter, cargo and aircraft maintenance operations. World laid off over 1500 employees, and is currently being restructured with an eventual goal of returning to profitability. N408BN, a 727-200, is seen here sporting the airline's new livery. Douglas DC-10 aircraft are operated, as well as the Boeing type.
(Udo and Birgit Schaefer Collection)

Yemania (IY)

Yemania was formed in 1954 as the national airline of the then Kingdom of Yemen. Operations began with a domestic network, linking the Red Sea to Djibouti, utilising Douglas DC-3 aircraft. Today scheduled passenger services are maintained with a Boeing fleet, with international operations to the UK, Netherlands, France, West Germany, Italy, Cyprus, India, Ethiopia, Bahrain, Egypt and other Middle Eastern destinations. Yemania is owned 50 per cent by the government, and 49 per cent by Saudia. Two DHC-7s are utilised on domestic services. 4W-ACJ, a Series 200 Advanced Boeing 727, is seen here at Frankfurt.

(Udo and Birgit Schaefer Collection)

Ansett Airlines of Australia (AN)

Ansett Airlines was founded in February 1936 by Reginald Miles Ansett. The company was formed after Ansett had been forced by the Victoria Transport Board to discontinue his omnibus service between Melbourne and Hamilton. An inaugural flight using a Fokker Universal was made on 17 February of that year, over the same route. Today Ansett is the largest domestic carrier in Australia, serving every state capital. In 1980, the company was taken over by News Ltd, the Rupert Murdoch company that owns newspapers and television companies. Ansett operates a fleet of Boeing 727, 737, 767, F-27 and Fokker 50 aircraft. The Boeing 727-200F seen here is sporting the livery of Ansett Air Freight, a subsidiary company.

(Udo and Birgit Schaefer Collection)